Connected Mathematics 2

Common Core Investigations
Teacher's Guide

Grade Seven

PEARSON

Boston, Massachusetts
Upper Saddle River, New Jersey

Common Core State Standards: © Copyright 2010. National Governors Association Center for Best Practices and Council of Chief State School Officers. All rights reserved.

Connected Mathematics™ is a trademark of Michigan State University.

Pearson Prentice Hall™ is a registered trademark of Pearson Education, Inc.

Pearson® is a registered trademark of Pearson plc.

Prentice Hall® is a registered trademark of Pearson Education, Inc.

ExamView® is a registered trademark of eInstruction Corporation.

TeacherExpress™ is a trademark of Pearson Education, Inc.

13-digit ISBN 978-0-13-318383-2

10-digit ISBN 0-13-318383-1

4 5 6 7 8 9 10 V042 15 14 13 12

Table of Contents

Common Core Investigations Teacher's Guide
Grade 7

CMP and the Common Core State Standards

Connected Mathematics (CMP) is a field-tested and research-validated program that focuses on a few big ideas at each grade level. Students explore these ideas in depth, thereby developing deep understanding of key ideas that they carry from one grade to the next. The sequencing of topics within a grade and from grade to grade, the result of lengthy field-testing and validation, helps to ensure the development of students' deep mathematical understanding and strong problem-solving skills. By the end of grade 8, CMP students will have studied all of the content and skills in the Common Core State Standards for Mathematics* (CCSSM) for middle grades (Grades 6-8). The focus on helping students develop deep mathematical understanding and strong problem solving skills aligns well to the intent of the Common Core State Standards for Mathematics, which articulates 3 to 5 areas of emphasis at each grade level from Kindergarten through Grade 8.

The sequence of content and skills in CMP varies in some instances from that in the CCSSM, so in collaboration with the CMP2 authors, Pearson has created a set of investigations for each grade level to further support and fully develop students' understanding of the content standards of the CCSSM. The authors are confident that the CMP2 curriculum supplemented with the additional investigations at each grade level will address all of the content and skills of the CCSSM, but even more, will contribute significantly to advancing students' mathematical proficiency as described in the Standards for Mathematical Practices of the CCSSM. Through the in-depth exploration of concepts, students become confident in solving a variety of problems with flexibility, skill, and insightfulness, and are able to communicate their reasoning and understanding in a variety of ways.

In this supplement, you will find support for all of the Common Core (CC) Investigations.

- The At-A-Glance page includes Teaching Notes and answers to all problems and exercises for the CC Investigation.

- The Additional Practice and Skill Practice pages can be reproduced for your students. These offer opportunities for students to reinforce the core concepts of the CC Investigation.

- Use the Check-Up to assess your students' understanding of the concepts presented in the investigation.

- The answers for all of the ancillary pages are found at the back of this book.

- The reduced student pages are provided for your convenience as you read through the teaching support and plan for implementing each investigation.

In the Pacing Guide (pp. xii–xiii), we propose placement for teaching each CC Investigations. CC Investigations 1–3 build on the concepts of linear relationships, so they should be taught after *Moving Straight Ahead.* CC Investigation 4 involves geometric concepts, so it should be used after the unit *Filling and Wrapping.* CC Investigation 5 on Sampling couples well with *Data Distributions* Investigation 1.

Common Core State Standards Correlations

The following alignment of the Common Core State Standards for Mathematics to Pearson's *Connected Mathematics 2* (CMP2) ©2009 program includes the supplemental investigations that complete the CMP2 program.

COMMON CORE STATE STANDARDS GRADE 7	CMP2 UNITS	CONTENT
Ratios and Proportional Relationships		
Analyze proportional relationships and use them to solve real-world and mathematical problems.		
7.RP.1 Compute unit rates associated with ratios of fractions, including ratios of lengths, areas and other quantities measured in like or different units.	*CC Investigations*	**CC Inv. 1:** Graphing Proportions
7.RP.2 Recognize and represent proportional relationships between quantities.	*Comparing and Scaling*	**Inv. 1:** Making Comparisons **Inv. 2:** Comparing Ratios, Percents, and Fractions **Inv. 3:** Comparing and Scaling Rates **Inv. 4:** Making Sense of Proportions
7.RP.2.a Decide whether two quantities are in a proportional relationship, e.g., by testing for equivalent ratios in a table or graphing on a coordinate plane and observing whether the graph is a straight line through the origin.	*Comparing and Scaling* *CC Investigations*	**Inv. 4:** Making Sense of Proportions **CC Inv. 1:** Graphing Proportions
7.RP.2.b Identify the constant of proportionality (unit rate) in tables, graphs, equations, diagrams, and verbal descriptions of proportional relationships.	*Comparing and Scaling* *Moving Straight Ahead*	**Inv. 3:** Comparing and Scaling Rates **Inv. 4:** Making Sense of Proportions **Inv. 1:** Walking Rates **Inv. 2:** Exploring Linear Functions With Graphs and Tables **Inv. 3:** Solving Equations **Inv. 4:** Exploring Slope

COMMON CORE STATE STANDARDS GRADE 7	CMP2 UNITS	CONTENT
7.RP.2.c Represent proportional relationships by equations.	*Variables and Patterns*	**Inv. 1:** Variables, Tables, and Coordinate Graphs **Inv. 2:** Analyzing Graphs and Tables **Inv. 3:** Rules and Equations **Inv. 4:** ACE 13
	Comparing and Scaling	**Inv. 4:** Making Sense of Proportions
	Stretching and Shrinking	**Inv. 4:** Similarity and Ratios **Inv. 5:** Using Similar Triangles and Rectangles
	Moving Straight Ahead	**Inv. 1:** Walking Rates **Inv. 2:** Exploring Linear Functions With Graphs and Tables **Inv. 3:** Solving Equations **Inv. 4:** Exploring Slope
7.RP.2.d Explain what a point (x, y) on the graph of a proportional relationship means in terms of the situation, with special attention to the points $(0, 0)$ and $(1, r)$ where r is the unit rate.	*Variables and Patterns*	**Inv. 2:** Analyzing Graphs and Tables
	Comparing and Scaling	**Inv. 3:** ACE 9, 10
	Moving Straight Ahead	**Inv. 1:** Walking Rates **Inv. 2:** Exploring Linear Functions With Graphs and Tables **Inv. 3:** Solving Equations **Inv. 4:** Exploring Slope
	CC Investigations	**CC Inv. 1:** Graphing Proportions
7.RP.3 Use proportional relationships to solve multistep ratio and percent problems. Examples: simple interest, tax, markups and markdowns, gratuities and commissions, fees, percent increase and decrease, percent error.	*Variables and Patterns*	**Inv. 4:** ACE 12
	Comparing and Scaling	**Inv. 1:** Making Comparisons **Inv. 2:** Comparing Ratios, Percents, and Fractions **Inv. 3:** Comparing and Scaling Rates **Inv. 4:** Making Sense of Proportions
	Stretching and Shrinking	**Inv. 4:** Similarity and Ratios **Inv. 5:** Using Similar Triangles and Rectangles

COMMON CORE STATE STANDARDS GRADE 7	CMP2 UNITS	CONTENT
The Number System		
Apply and extend previous understandings of operations with fractions to add, subtract, multiply, and divide rational numbers.		
7.NS.1 Apply and extend previous understandings of addition and subtraction to add and subtract rational numbers; represent addition and subtraction on a horizontal or vertical number line diagram.	*Accentuate the Negative*	**Inv. 2:** Adding and Subtracting Integers **Inv. 4:** Properties of Operations
7.NS.1.a Descrie situations in which opposite quantities combine to make 0.	*Accentuate the Negative*	**Inv. 2:** Adding and Subtracting Integers
7.NS.1.b Understand $p + q$ as the number located a distance $|q|$ from p, in the positive or negative direction depending on whether q is positive or negative. Show that a number and its opposite have a sum of 0 (are additive inverses). Interpret sums of rational numbers by describing real-world contexts.	*Accentuate the Negative*	**Inv. 1:** Extending the Number System **Inv. 2:** Adding and Subtracting Integers
7.NS.1.c Understand subtraction of rational numbers as adding the additive inverse, $p - q = p + (-q)$. Show that the distance between two rational numbers on the number line is the absolute value of their difference, and apply this principle in real-world contexts.	*Accentuate the Negative*	**Inv. 2:** Adding and Subtracting Integers
7.NS.1.d Apply properties of operations as strategies to add and subtract rational numbers.	*Accentuate the Negative*	**Inv. 2:** Adding and Subtracting Integers **Inv. 4:** Properties of Operations
7.NS.2 Fluently divide multi-digit numbers using the standard algorithm.	*Accentuate the Negative*	**Inv. 3:** Multiplying and Dividing Integers **Inv. 4:** Properties of Operations
7.NS.2.a Understand that multiplication is extended from fractions to rational numbers by requiring that operations continue to satisfy the properties of operations, particularly the distributive property, leading to products such as $(-1)(-1) = 1$ and the rules for multiplying signed numbers. Interpret products of rational numbers by describing real-world contexts.	*Accentuate the Negative*	**Inv. 3:** Multiplying and Dividing Integers **Inv. 4:** Properties of Operations
7.NS.2.b Understand that integers can be divided, provided that the divisor is not zero, and every quotient of integers (with non-zero divisor) is a rational number. If p and q are integers, then $-(p/q) = (-p)/q = p/(-q)$. Interpret quotients of rational numbers by describing real-world contexts.	*Accentuate the Negative*	**Inv. 3:** Multiplying and Dividing Integers
7.NS.2.c Apply properties of operations as strategies to multiply and divide rational numbers.	*Accentuate the Negative*	**Inv. 3:** Multiplying and Dividing Integers **Inv. 4:** Properties of Operations
7.NS.2 .d Convert a rational number to a decimal using long division; know that the decimal form of a rational number terminates in 0s or eventually repeats	*Comparing and Scaling* *Accentuate the Negative*	**Inv. 3:** Comparing and Scaling Rates **Inv. 3:** Multiplying and Dividing Integers
7.NS.3 Solve real-world and mathematical problems involving the four operations with rational numbers. NOTE: Computations with rational numbers extend the rules for manipulating fractions to complex fractions.	*Accentuate the Negative*	**Inv. 2:** Adding and Subtracting Integers **Inv. 3:** Multiplying and Dividing Integers **Inv. 4:** Properties of Operations

COMMON CORE STATE STANDARDS GRADE 7	CMP2 UNITS	CONTENT
Expressions and Equations		
Use properties of operations to generate equivalent expressions.		
7.EE.1 Apply properties of operations as strategies to add, subtract, factor, and expand linear expressions with rational coefficients.	*Moving Straight Ahead* *CC Investigations*	**Inv. 3:** Solving Equations **Inv. 4:** Exploring Slope **CC Inv. 2:** Equivalent Expressions
7.EE.2 Understand that rewriting an expression in different forms in a problem context can shed light on the problem and how the quantities in it are related.	*CC Investigations*	**CC Inv. 2:** Equivalent Expressions
7.EE.3 Solve multi-step real-life and mathematical problems posed with positive and negative rational numbers in any form (whole numbers, fractions, and decimals), using tools strategically. Apply properties of operations to calculate with numbers in any form; convert between forms as appropriate; and assess the reasonableness of answers using mental computation and estimation strategies.	*Variables and Patterns* *Accentuate the Negative* *Moving Straight Ahead*	**Inv. 2:** Analyzing Graphs and Tables **Inv. 3:** Rules and Equations **Inv. 4:** Calculator Tables and Graphs **Inv. 1:** Extending the Number System **Inv. 2:** Adding and Subtracting Integers **Inv. 3:** Multiplying and Dividing Integers **Inv. 4:** Properties of Operations **Inv. 1:** Walking Rates **Inv. 2:** Exploring Linear Functions With Graphs and Tables **Inv. 3:** Solving Equations **Inv. 4:** Exploring Slope
7.EE.4 Use variables to represent quantities in a real-world or mathematical problem, and construct simple equations and inequalities to solve problems by reasoning about the quantities.	*Variables and Patterns* *Moving Straight Ahead*	**Inv. 1:** Variables, Tables, and Coordinate Graphs **Inv. 2:** Analyzing Graphs and Tables **Inv. 3:** Rules and Equations **Inv. 1:** Walking Rates **Inv. 2:** Exploring Linear Functions With Graphs and Tables **Inv. 3:** Solving Equations **Inv. 4:** Exploring Slope
7.EE.4.a Solve word problems leading to equations of the form $px + q = r$ and $p(x + q) = r$, where p, q, and r are specific rational numbers. Solve equations of these forms fluently. Compare an algebraic solution to an arithmetic solution, identifying the sequence of the operations used in each approach.	*Variables and Patterns* *Moving Straight Ahead*	**Inv. 1:** Variables, Tables, and Coordinate Graphs **Inv. 2:** Analyzing Graphs and Tables **Inv. 3:** Rules and Equations **Inv. 1:** Walking Rates **Inv. 2:** Exploring Linear Functions With Graphs and Tables **Inv. 3:** Solving Equations **Inv. 4:** Exploring Slope
7.EE.4.b Solve word problems leading to inequalities of the form $px + q > r$ or $px + q < r$, where p, q, and r are specific rational numbers. Graph the solution set of the inequality and interpret it in the context of the problem.	*Moving Straight Ahead* *CC Investigations*	**Inv. 2:** ACE 44 **CC Inv. 3:** Inequalities

Check-Up

1. Sahil found 4 different stores that sell seeds for the flowers he wants to plant in his garden. The number of seeds per packet and the packet price for each store are shown below.

Andy's Seeds	Jenny's Seeds	Garden Place	Blooming Acres
10 flower seeds $2.50	12 flower seeds $3.12	20 flower seeds $4.60	15 flower seeds $3.60

a. Write the rate of seeds to dollars for each store. Then write a unit rate for each.

b. Sahil needs 75 flower seeds for his garden. He wants to spend the least amount of money and have the fewest seeds left over. Where should Sahil buy his seeds? Explain your answer.

c. Sahil's friend has $10 and wants to buy as many seeds as he can. Where should Sahil's friend buy his seeds? Explain.

2. Four students are reading the same 200-page book. On Monday night, they record the numbers of pages they have read and the time it took them.

Name	Pages Read	Time (min)
Emilio	15	20
Luz	8	10
Erika	3	5
Jerome	7	10

Emilio says that he'll finish his book in the shortest amount of time, since he read the most pages. Is he correct? Explain why or why not.

Check-Up *(continued)*

3. The table shows the prices for different lengths of rescue rope.

Rescue Rope (8,000-lb Strength)				
Length (ft)	4	8	12	20
Price ($)	6	12	18	30

a. Graph the data pairs from the table and connect the points. Describe the shape the graph takes.

b. Where does the graph cross the *y*-axis? Write the data pair represented by that point and explain what the point means.

c. What price value corresponds on the graph to a length value of 1 ft? What does that data pair mean in terms of the price of the rescue rope?

4. The table shows the prices for different lengths of a stronger rescue rope.

Rescue Rope (13,000-lb Strength)				
Length (ft)	8	9	15	30
Price ($)	20	22.5	37.5	75

a. Write the unit rate for this rope in dollars per foot.

b. Explain how the graph of the data pairs from this table would be different than the graph you made in Part 3. Explain how the graphs would be similar.

CC Investigation 1: Graphing Proportions

Problem 1.1

During the first basketball game of the season, Karl made 3 of his 5 free-throw attempts. Karl then made 3 of 5 free-throw attempts in each of the second game, the third game, the fourth game, and the fifth game.

A. Copy and complete the table.

Karl's Free Throws					
Game Number	1	2	3	4	5
Total Number of Free-throw Attempts	5	10	■	■	■
Total Number of Free Throws Made	3	■	■	■	■

B. For each game, you can write the coordinates of the point (*free-throw attempts, free throws made*). The first point is (5, 3).

   1. List the coordinates of the other four points. Graph all five points.

   2. What do you notice about these points? If the pattern continues for 20 games, how many free throws will Karl attempt? How many free throws will he make? Explain.

   3. What *y*-value on the graph corresponds to the *x*-value of 0? Explain in words what this point represents.

   4. What *y*-value on the graph corresponds to the *x*-value of 1? What does this point, $(1, r)$ represent?

   5. Connect the points. What is the slope of the line? Explain how you found the slope.

Notes _____
_____
_____
_____

A **rate** is a ratio that compares quantities in different units such as miles to hours. An example of a rate is $\frac{140 \text{ miles}}{3.5 \text{ hours}}$.

A **unit rate** is a rate for which one of the numbers being compared is 1 unit. So, $\frac{140 \text{ miles}}{3.5 \text{ hours}}$ is 140 miles ÷ 3.5 hours, or 40 miles per 1 hour. The rate of miles to hours becomes miles per hour, which is written mi/h. The word "per" can be replaced with "for one."

Problem 1.2

A. On a recent road trip, the team van traveled 640 miles on 19 gallons of gasoline.

  1. What is the rate of miles to gallons?

  2. What is the rate of miles to one gallon?

B. The team wants to sell mini basketballs to raise money. The table shows different package sizes for purchasing basketballs.

Mini Basketballs	
Price	Quantity
$9.98	12
$17.98	25
$39.99	50

  1. What is the rate of dollars per balls for each package size?

  2. What is the rate of dollars to one ball for each package size?

C. A 6-pack of basketballs weighs $8\frac{1}{4}$ pounds.

  1. What is the rate of pounds to balls?

  2. What is the rate of pounds to one ball?

D. 1. What information does a unit rate provide?

  2. Describe how you can find a unit rate. Use an example to illustrate your method.

Two quantities are in a **proportional relationship** if a change in one quantity corresponds to a change by the same factor in the other quantity. The ratios between the quantities do not change when the quantities themselves change.

Notes _____

_____

_____

_____

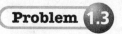
Karl stays in shape between basketball seasons by jogging. The table shows his distances and times for one week.

Karl's Jogging					
Day	Mon.	Tues.	Wed.	Thurs.	Sat.
Distance (in miles)	3	5	4.5	12	13.5
Time (in hours)	0.6	1	0.9	2.4	2.7

A. Use the information in the table.

   1. Describe any pattern you see in how the distances and times are related.

   2. Find the ratio of miles per hour for each day.

   3. What do you notice about the ratios? What does that tell you about Karl's jogging?

   4. Explain how to use the ratios to find how far Karl can jog in 1.5 hours.

B. Graph the data pairs from the table. Plot distance along the vertical axis and time along the horizontal axis.

   1. Connect the data points and describe the shape the graph takes. What does this tell you about the relationship between distance and time?

   2. What value on the horizontal axis corresponds on the graph to a vertical value of 1.5? What does this mean in terms of Karl's jogging?

   3. a. Where does the line of the graph cross the vertical axis? Write the data pair represented by that point.

     b. Explain what that point means.

C. Karl's jogging speed in miles per hour is a unit rate, r.

   1. Explain how to use the table to find Karl's jogging speed, r.

   2. Look at the point $(1, r)$ on the graph. Does that point lie on the line you drew to represent Karl's jogging data?

   3. Explain what point $(1, r)$ represents.

   4. Suppose Karl begins jogging faster, and jogs 3 miles in 0.5 hour one day, and 8 miles in $1\frac{1}{3}$ hours another day. If these points were graphed, and a line drawn through them, what y-value would correspond to an x-value of 1? What would that point represent?

Notes _____

_____

_____

_____

Exercises

1. **a.** In the first step of a number puzzle, you multiply your starting number by 3. If you start with 8, what is the new number after Step 1?

   b. What are the new numbers after Step 1 for the following starting numbers: 2, 4, 5, 6, and 7?

   c. Graph the (*starting number, Step 1 number*) points using the numbers from part (b).

   d. Step 2 of the puzzle is to take the Step 1 number and multiply that number by 3. Copy and complete the table below.

Puzzle Numbers

Starting Number	5	6	8	9	10	12	15
Step 1 Number	■	■	24	■	■	■	■
Step 2 Number	■	■	72	■	■	■	■

   e. Graph the (*starting number, Step 2 number*) points. What do you notice?

   f. If the graphs in parts (c) and (e) are drawn using the same scales, would the graph in part (e) be *more steep* or *less steep* than the graph in (c)?

For Exercises 2–7, write the comparison as a rate. Then find the unit rate.

2. 759 miles per 22 gallons

3. $3.01 for 1.21 pounds of nectarines

4. $25.92 for 12 key chains

5. 72 phone calls in 6 hours

6. 2,220 Calories in 6 servings

7. $270 for 144 American Flag patches

8. **a.** Find the unit price for each size of packaging.

   b. Which size offers the best unit price?

   c. Find the new unit price for the 8-pack if it goes on sale for $1.99.

   d. What is the least expensive way to buy 24 bottles of water during the sale period?

Bottled Water	
Price	Quantity
$2.19	4
$3.59	8
$6.99	24

Notes

_____

_____

_____

_____

9. Canned soup is marked at 3 for $3.99.

    a. What is the price per can?

    b. How many cans of soup can you buy for $1?

    c. How many cans of soup can you buy with $22?

10. For a report, Amanda must read 168 pages in 7 days.

    a. What are the two unit rates that she might compute?

    b. Compute each unit rate and tell what it means.

    c. Amanda plans to read the same number of pages each day. How many pages should Amanda have read by the end of the third day?

    d. If she has read 144 pages by day 5, can she expect to finish in time? Explain.

For Exercises 11–14, tell whether the table or graph represents a proportional relationship. Explain how you know.

11.

x	1	2	3	4
y	4	8	16	32

12.

x	1	3	5	7
y	2	6	10	14

13.

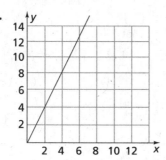

14.

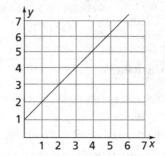

Notes _____

_____

_____

_____

15. The table shows the numbers of hours Melissa works and the amounts that she earns.

Melissa's Earnings					
Hours Worked	2	4	7	8	10
Earnings (in $)	44	88	154	176	220

   a. Write a ratio for each data pair in the table.

   b. Is the relationship between time and earnings proportional? Explain why or why not.

   c. Graph the data pairs from the table. Plot time along the horizontal axis and earnings along the vertical axis.

   d. What does the point $(0, 0)$ on the graph represent?

   e. Use the graph to determine how much Melissa earns per hour, r. Explain how you used the graph to find your answer.

   f. Give the ordered pair that represents Melissa's rate per hour.

   g. How much does Melissa earn if she works 6 hours?

16. The table shows Rebecca's jogging times and distances for one week.

Rebecca's Jogging					
Day	Mon.	Tues.	Wed.	Thurs.	Sat.
Distance (in miles)	2	4	6	3	10
Time (in hours)	0.3	0.7	1	0.5	2

   a. Describe any pattern you see in how the distances and times are related.

   b. Find the ratio of miles per hour for each day.

   c. What do you notice about the ratios? What does that tell you about Rebecca's jogging?

   d. Explain whether you can use the ratios to find how far Rebecca can jog in 1.5 hours.

Notes _____

_____

_____

_____

CC Investigation 2: Equivalent Expressions

Mathematical Goals

© **DOMAIN:** Expressions and Equations

- Apply the properties of operations to add, subtract, factor, and expand algebraic expressions.

- Understand that writing an equivalent expression in a problem context can shed light on how quantities in the problem are related.

Teaching Notes

In order for students to understand and appreciate the purpose of finding equivalent expressions, they first must understand that algebraic expressions can be written to represent problem situations. Give students practice in writing simple algebraic expressions by having them represent these situations:

- 3 more than a number
- 8 degrees less than yesterday's temperature
- some boxes of pencils with 25 pencils in each box
- splitting the cost of dinner equally among 4 friends

Have students explain what each value in their expressions represents.

Before beginning the problems, review the associative, commutative, and distributive properties, using different types of rational numbers.

Vocabulary
- algebraic expression
- associative property
- commutative property
- distributive property

Associative Property

$4 + (3 + 8) = (4 + 3) + 8$ $(3 \times 7.5) \times 2 = 3 \times (7.5 \times 2)$

Commutative Property

$\dfrac{1}{4} + \dfrac{3}{8} = \dfrac{3}{8} + \dfrac{1}{4}$ $4 \times \dfrac{5}{6} = \dfrac{5}{6} \times 4$

Distributive Property

$6 \times (8.5 + 9) = (6 \times 8.5) + (6 \times 9)$

Problem 2.1

During Problem 2.1 A, ask: *Why would you want to simplify the expression 25j + 11.5(2 + j)?* (to make it easier to find the value of the expression when given a value for *j*)

During Problem 2.1 A, guide students through the steps of the simplification. Ask:

- *How is the second expression different than the first?* (The coefficient 11.5 has been multiplied separately by each addend inside the parentheses.)
- *What property does that demonstrate?* (distributive property)
- *How is the third expression different than the second?* (The order of the addends is changed.)
- *What property does that demonstrate?* (commutative property)
- *How is the fourth expression different than the third?* (The coefficients of *j* have been placed together inside parentheses.)
- *What property does that demonstrate?* (distributive property)

Before Problem 2.1 A, Part 4, explain that to evaluate an expression, students should substitute the given value for *j* and then simplify.

After Problem 2.1, ask: *Was it easier to evaluate the expression in Part 4 or in Part 5? Why?* (Part 5 was easier to evaluate because there were fewer terms.)

Problem 2.2

Before 2.2 A, review with students how to express a percent as an equivalent decimal. Ask: *What decimal is equivalent to 20%?* (0.2)

During Problem 2.2 A, ask: *What equivalent expression can you write for p − 0.2p, using the distributive property?* ($p(1 - 0.2)$)

During Problem 2.2 A, Part 4, ask:

- *What expression can you write to represent the sale price of an item that is 25% off?* ($p - 0.25p$)
- *What equivalent expression can you write using the distributive property?* ($p(1 - 0.25)$)
- *What expression can you write to represent the price of an item that is on sale for 75% of its original price?* ($0.75p$)

During Problem 2.2 C, ask: *How can you tell from looking at the expression which term represents the discount and which represents the tax?* (The term being subtracted represents a discount off the original price, while the term being added represents the tax added to the price.)

Summarize

To summarize the lesson, ask:

- *When might you use a property of operations to write an equivalent expression?* (to simplify an expression so that you can evaluate it using mental math)
- *What property is used to rewrite the expression 3.6a + 4.4a as (3.6 + 4.4)a?* (distributive property)
- *What is another way to express 0.7 times a number?* (the number minus 0.3 times the number)

Assignment Guide for Investigation 2

Problem 2.1, Exercises 1–17
Problem 2.2, Exercises 18–23

Answers to Investigation 2

Problem 2.1

A. 1. the cost of the pairs of jeans Chris buys

2. $11.5(2 + j)$

3.

Step	Reason
$25j + 11.5(2 + j)$	original expression
$25j + 11.5(2) + 11.5(j)$	distributive property
$25j + 11.5(j) + 11.5(2)$	commutative property of addition
$(25 + 11.5)j + 11.5(2)$	distributive property
$(36.5)j + 11.5(2)$	addition
$36.5j + 23$	multiplication

4. For 2 pairs of jeans: $25j + 11.5(2 + j) = 25(2) + 11.5(2 + 2) = 50 + 11.5(4) = 50 + 46 = \$96$; for 4 pairs of jeans: $25j + 11.5(2 + j) = 25(4) + 11.5(2 + 4) = 100 + 11.5(6) = 100 + 69 = \$169$.

5. For 2 pairs of jeans: $36.5j + 23 = 36.5(2) + 23 = 73 + 23 = \$96$; for 4 pairs of jeans: $36.5j + 23 = 36.5(4) + 23 = 146 + 23 = \$169$; the expressions have the same values for a given value of j, so the expressions are equivalent.

B. 1. 78 represents the money Chris has; $20t$ represents the cost of t dress shirts; $\frac{1}{2}(12t)$ is the cost of t ties at $\frac{1}{2}$ off.

2.

Step	Reason
$78 - 20t - \frac{1}{2}(12t)$	original expression
$78 - 20t - 6t$	multiplication
$78 - (20 + 6)t$	distributive property
$78 - 26t$	addition

3. $78 - 20t - \frac{1}{2}(12t) = 78 - 60 - 18 = 0$;

$78 - 26t = 78 - 78 = 0$; yes, the expressions have the same value for $t = 3$ because they are equivalent expressions.

Problem 2.2

A. 1. p represents the full price of the item; $0.2p$ represents the 20% discount.

2. The sale price is the full price, p, minus the 20% discount, or $p - 0.2p$.

3. Yes, according to the distributive property, $p - 0.2p = (1 - 0.2)p = 0.8p$.

4. The sales are equivalent. A sale of 25% off gives a sale price of $100\% - 25\% = 75\%$.

B. 1. c represents the price of an item; $0.06c$ represents the 6% sales tax on the item.

2. The price, including tax, is the item's price, c, plus the tax, $0.06c$, or $c + 0.06c$.

3. Factor c out of both terms, and then add the remaining terms: $c + 0.06c = (1 + 0.06)c = 1.06c$.

4. The expressions are equivalent: $c + 0.06c = 1.06c$.

5. $c + 0.06c = 20 + (0.06)20 = 20 + 1.2 = \$21.20$; $1.06c = 1.06(20) = \$21.20$; The expressions have the same value because the they are equivalent.

6. The cost of the jacket with tax is $1.06c = 1.06(225) = \$238.50$; $\$235 < \$238.50$, so it would cost Chris less to buy the jacket online.

C. 1. 15%; the term $-0.15d$ represents a savings of 15% of the original price, d.

2. 7%; the term $+0.07d$ represents a tax of 7% on the original price, d.

3. $d - 0.15d + 0.07d = (1 - 0.15 + 0.07)d = 0.92d$

Exercises

1.

Step	Reason
$4(p + 7) - 2p$	original expression
$4p + 28 - 2p$	distributive property
$4p - 2p + 28$	commutative property
$(4 - 2)p + 28$	distributive property
$2p + 28$	subtraction

2. $10t$; distributive property

3. $\frac{5}{3}x$; distributive property

4. $15m - 55$; distributive property

5. $4p - 12$; distributive property, commutative property

6. $1.2n + 8.4$; distributive property, commutative property

7. $-2g + 4h - 22$; distributive property, commutative property, associative property

8. $4(x - 3)$; $4(-3 + x)$

9. a. $2m + 20$, where m represents the amount of money Marty has.

b. $m + 2m + 20 = (1 + 2)m + 20 = 3m + 20$; distributive property

c. $\frac{1}{2}(3m + 20) = \frac{3}{2}m + 10$; distributive property

d. Aimee: $2m + 20 = 2(30) + 20 = \$80$;

Jack: $\frac{3}{2}m + 10 = \frac{3}{2}(30) + 10 = 45 + 10 = \$55$

10. No, $x + 8 + 3x + 12y = 4x + 8 + 12y$; $4(x + 8) + 12y = 4x + 32 + 12y$; $4x + 8 + 12y \neq 4x + 32 + 12y$.

11. first week: 8; second week: h; third week: $2h$; total: $8 + h + 2h = 8 + 3h$

12. D

13. B

14. F

15. E

16. A

17. C

18. a. $w + 0.07w$

b. $1.07w$

19. $d + 0.04d$; $1.04d$

20. $x - 0.25x$; $0.75x$

21. $c + 0.75c$; $1.75c$

22. Yes, $0.83p = (1 - 0.17)p = p - 0.17p$.

23. Yes, $y - \frac{1}{5}y = \left(1 - \frac{1}{5}\right)y = \frac{4}{5}y$.

When the solution of an inequality requires dividing or multiplying by a negative number, you need to change the direction of the inequality sign. Compare these solutions.

$$12x < 60 \qquad -12x < 60$$

$$\frac{12x}{12} < \frac{60}{12} \qquad \frac{-12x}{-12} > \frac{60}{-12}$$

$$x < 5 \qquad x > -5$$

- Choose a number included in the solution to $12x < 60$. Is this also a solution to $-12x < 60$? Explain.

Problem 3.3

A. The community center has $175 to spend on video games for its new game system. Games are on sale for $35 each.

   1. The inequality $175 - 35g \geq 0$ represents the number of games the center could buy. Solve the inequality and explain the solution.

   2. Graph the solution on a number line.

   3. Explain why a value of g that is less than 0 does not make sense for this situation.

B. The center is considering signing up for an online game-rental service rather than buying the games. The table shows the equipment cost and monthly fees for two services.

Game Rental Services		
Service	**Equipment Cost**	**Monthly Fee**
NetGames	$99	$8
Anytime Games	$19	$19

   1. The inequality $175 - 8m \geq 99$ represents the number of months the center could rent games from NetGames with its $175. Solve the inequality and explain the solution.

   2. Graph the solution on a number line.

   3. Write and solve an inequality to represent the number of months the center could rent games from Anytime Games.

   4. Which service should the community center use? Explain your choice.

Notes _____

_____

_____

_____

Exercises

For Exercises 1–4, use the information below.

Amusement Park Rides Height Requirements			
Ride	Height Requirement	Ride	Height Requirement
Jungle Jam	minimum of 40 in.	The Spiral	more than 35 in.
Tilt-a-Whirl	at least 48 in.	Ladybug	under 46 in.
Stargazer	more than 44 in.	Leapin' Lizard	at least 38 in.
Bunny Hop	60 in. maximum	Racetrack	over 42 in.

1. Write and graph an inequality that represents the heights of people who can ride the Tilt-a-Whirl.

2. Write and graph an inequality that represents the heights of people who can ride the Ladybug.

3. Is it possible that someone is able to ride the Spiral but not the Leapin' Lizard? If so, give that person's height.

4. Would someone be able to ride both the Tilt-a-Whirl and the Ladybug? Explain your answer.

5. Playing a video game, Emily has gained some points, lost 107 points, and finishes at less than 800 points. The inequality $p - 107 < 800$ represents this situation. Solve and graph the inequality.

6. **Multiple Choice** On level 2 of a video game, the maximum number of points is 1,000. Emily has lost 279 points and is on level 2. The inequality $p - 279 \leq 1,000$ represents this situation. Which is the graph of its solution?

A.

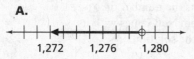

C.

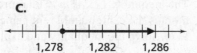

B.

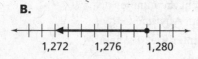

D.

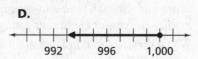

Notes _____

_____

_____

_____

For Exercises 7–9, use the information below.

Florida Hiking Trails		
Trail	**Location**	**Length**
Citrus Hiking Trail	Withlacoochee State Forest	43.3 miles
Myakka Hiking Trail	Myakka River State Park	49 miles
Big Oak Trail	Suwannee River State Park	12.5 miles
Florida Trail	Ocala National Forest	71 miles

7. Camille has a goal of hiking more than 350 miles this year. She already hiked the Florida Trail and now plans to hike 9 miles each day for d days. The inequality $9d + 71 > 350$ represents this situation. Solve and graph the inequality.

8. **Multiple Choice** Camille's brother Roberto hiked the Florida Trail with her and the Myakka Hiking Trail alone. He wants to hike no more than 400 miles this year and now plans to hike d day trips of 10 miles each. Which inequality could represent this situation?

   A. $10d + 120 > 400$ **C.** $10d + 120 \leq 400$

   B. $10d + 120 \geq 400$ **D.** $10d + 120 < 400$

9. Miquel does all of his hiking on the Big Oak Trail. He already has hiked it 3 times this year and has a goal of hiking at least 75 total miles this year. Write and solve an inequality representing the number of times b he still needs to hike the Big Oak Trail to reach his goal.

10. Jenna has $39 to spend on materials to make pottery figures. It costs her $4 to make one figure. Write and solve an inequality to represent this situation.

Notes _____

_____

_____

_____

For Exercises 11–20, solve and graph each inequality.

11. $x + 7 < 9$

12. $y - 12 \geq 3$

13. $7z - 49 > 98$

14. $3a - 5 \leq 13$

15. $-2b < 10$

16. $-5c \geq -55$

17. $p + 6.8 \geq 14$

18. $36 < -1.8y$

19. $\dfrac{1}{2} - 2x > 1$

20. $4\dfrac{1}{4} \leq 5t + \dfrac{3}{4}$

21. Multiple Choice Which is the solution to the inequality $3x - 12 > 9$?

A. $x > 21$ **B.** $x < 7$ **C.** $x > 7$ **D.** $x > 3$

22. Janine is in charge of painting her school's time capsule. Her school's time capsule has a surface area that is less than or equal to the surface area of the time capsule shown below.

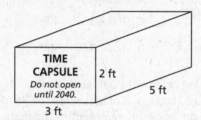

TIME CAPSULE
Do not open until 2040.

2 ft

5 ft

3 ft

Janine already painted 6 square feet and needs to buy more paint to finish. Write and solve an inequality to show how much more area Janine needs to paint.

23. A machinist making steel rods for an airplane engine knows that each rod must be at least 9 mm long but no longer than 9.5 mm.

a. Write two inequalities that together represent the possible lengths. Graph the inequalities.

b. Can both solutions be shown on one graph? If so, draw the graph.

Notes _____

_____

_____

_____

For Exercises 24–26, use the information below.

Triathlon Distances	
Race Portion	Distance
Swim	2.4 mi
Bike	112 mi
Run	26.2 mi

24. Pauline wants to finish the swim portion of the triathlon in 140 minutes or less. Write and solve an inequality to show the pace, in minutes per mile, that Pauline must swim.

25. Athletes are given 630 minutes to complete both the swim and bike portions of the race. Pauline finishes the swim portion in 70 minutes. She averages a rate of b minutes per mile on the bike. The inequality $112b + 70 \leq 630$ represents this situation. Solve the inequality and explain what the solution represents.

26. Pauline completes the swim and bike portions in 538 minutes. Her goal is to complete the entire triathlon in 800 minutes or less. The inequality $800 \geq 532 + 26.2r$ represents this situation, where r is the number of minutes it takes Pauline to run each mile. Graph the solution to the inequality.

27. **Multiple Choice** An electrician has a roll with 45 ft of wire. She uses $23\frac{1}{2}$ ft of the wire on one project, and will cut p 3-ft pieces from the rest of the roll. Which inequality represents this situation?

   A. $3p + 23\frac{1}{2} \geq 45$ **C.** $3p - 23\frac{1}{2} \leq 45$

   B. $3p + 23\frac{1}{2} \leq 45$ **D.** $3p - 23\frac{1}{2} \geq 45$

28. A bicycle shop rents bicycles for $3.50 per hour, and helmets for $6 per day. Martin has $20 to spend to rent a helmet and a bicycle for h hours. The graph shows the solution to the inequality $3.5h + 6 \leq 20$ representing this situation.

   Explain what the graph shows about how long Martin can rent the bicycle.

Inequalities   **17**

STUDENT PAGE

STUDENT PAGE

Notes

Inequalities   **(17)26**

CC Investigation 4: Geometry Topics

Mathematical Goals

- Draw possible triangles when given three measures of their angles or sides, noticing when the conditions determine a unique triangle, more than one triangle, or no triangle.

- Describe two-dimensional cross sections of three-dimensional figures.

- Use the formulas for the area and circumference of a circle to solve problems.

- Give an informal derivation of the relationship between a circle's area and its circumference.

- Use facts about complementary, vertical, and adjacent angles to write and solve simple equations for an unknown angle in a figure.

Teaching Notes

In this investigation, students will explore the geometry topics of cross sections, circles, drawing triangles, and special angle relationships.

You may want to have solids available to demonstrate cross sections. Students could create a table display of cross sections after you have cut these solids in different ways. Cutting solid shapes and then coloring the cuts is one way to help students understand what happens when solids are cut to make cross sections.

Review the parts of a circle using a diagram. Also, review the formulas for the circumference and area of a circle. When students are given the diameter of a circle, check that they are finding the radius before determining the area of the circle.

Drawing triangles with given conditions will require students to recall that the sum of the measures of the angles of any triangle is 180°. Also review with students the definition of similar figures and apply the definition to triangles. Students will use protractors and rulers to construct the triangles.

Students will use special relationships of complementary, vertical, and adjacent angles to find the missing measures of angles in a figure. The purpose of this investigation is to find the measures without actually measuring the angles, though giving students access to protractors will allow them to check their answers.

Vocabulary

- cross section
- diameter
- radius
- circumference
- complementary angles
- adjacent angles
- vertical angles

Materials

- geometric solids
- protractor
- ruler

Problem 4.1

Before Problem 4.1, distribute cylinder models to students, or display one for the class to examine. Ask:

- *What three-dimensional solid is this?* (cylinder)
- *What two-dimensional shape do you see when you look at one base?* (circle)
- *What two-dimensional shape do you seen when you look at the side of the cylinder from any direction?* (rectangle)
- *How is cutting a block of cheese like making a cross section?* (The resulting cut of a block of cheese reveals a cross section of the solid figure.)

During Problem 4.1, ask: *What shapes of cheese should Marcus serve on rectangular or circular crackers?* (rectangles or circles)

Problem 4.2

Before Problem 4.2, ask:

- *Why is the numerical value of π written followed by three dots?* (to show that it is not an exact value and the decimal digits go on forever with no repeating pattern)
- *What is another approximation of pi that you know?* $\left(\dfrac{22}{7}\right)$
- *If you want the answer for the circumference of a circle to be exact, what should you do?* (Leave π in the answer.)
- *Is the circumference a measure of length or of area?* (a measure of length)
- *Can two circles have the same radius but not have the same circumference?* (No, every circle with the same radius has the same circumference.)

After Problem 4.2, ask:

- *What type of units do you use to express area?* (square units)
- *Why can't you express the exact area of a circle using just numbers?* (because the value used for π is an approximation)
- *Use the ratio you wrote for Part B to write the ratio of the circumference of the dessert plate to its area.* $\left(\dfrac{2}{r} = \dfrac{2}{6} = \dfrac{1}{3}\right)$

Problem 4.3

Before Problem 4.3, ask:

- *What do you know about the sum of the measures of the angles of any triangle?* (It is always 180°.)
- *How many different triangles with a given set of angle measures can be drawn?* (an infinite number)
- *What do you call two triangles which have the same angle measures, but different side lengths?* (similar)
- *What do you know about the side lengths of similar triangles?* (Their side lengths are proportional.)

During Problem 4.3 B, ask: *What do you know about the side lengths and angle measures of an isosceles triangle?* (Two of the sides are the same length, and two of the angles have the same measure.)

During Problem 4.3 C, ask: *From just looking at the sets, which measurements won't allow you to draw a triangle? If so, which one or ones?* (The side lengths of 2 in., 4 in., and 6 in. cannot make a triangle since the sum of the length of the two shorter sides is not greater than the length of the longest side. The angle measures of 20°, 40°, and 60° can not make a triangle since their sum is not 180°.)

Problem 4.4

Review the definitions of the types of angles. Remind students that *supplementary angles* are two angles which have a sum of measures of 180°.

During Problem 4.4, ask:

- *How do you know the measures of the outside corners of the piece of poster board?* (The poster board is a rectangle, so the measure of each angle is 90°.)
- *How do you know that the measures of ∠j and ∠h are equal?* (We are told that the triangle with angles d, h, and j is an isosceles triangle.)
- *What is the sum of the measures of angles that together form a straight line?* (180°)

Summarize

To summarize the lesson, ask:

- *What two-dimensional shapes can be made by taking a cross section parallel to any face of a right rectangular prism?* (rectangles)
- *What are the formulas that relate a circle's area and circumference to its radius?* ($A = \pi r^2$; $C = 2\pi r$)
- *What symbol does the expression for the area or circumference of a circle need to include for the measure to be exact?* (π)
- *How many different triangles could be drawn which have angle measures of 35°, 55°, and 90°?* (an infinite number)
- *How many different triangles could be drawn which have side lengths of 6 cm, 8 cm, and 10 cm* (1)
- *How many different triangles could be drawn which have angle measures of 70°, 70°, and 50°?* (0)
- *What is the sum of the measures of complementary angles?* (90°)
- *What is the measure of the angle that is vertical to an angle measuring 45°?* (45°)

Assignment Guide for Investigation 4

Problem 4.1, Exercises 1–8
Problem 4.2, Exercises 9–15
Problem 4.3, Exercises 16–28
Problem 4.4, Exercises 29–36

Answers to Investigation 4

Problem 4.1

A. **1.** Slice the rectangular block to make rectangular slices; slice the cylindrical block to make rectangular slices.

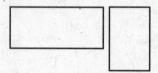

2. The sizes and shapes of the slices of the rectangular block would not change. The rectangular slices from the cylindrical block would change size and shape, getting larger toward the center of the block, and smaller toward the edges.

B. **1.** Slice the rectangular block to make square slices; slice the cylindrical block to make circular slices.

2. No; the sizes and shapes of the slices from the rectangular block would not change.

C. Marcus should cut the rectangular block into rectangular slices for the rectangular crackers and the cylindrical block into circular slices for the circular crackers so that the shapes of the slices match the shapes of the crackers. He also could slice the rectangular block into square slices to fit the circular crackers.

Problem 4.2

A. **1.** Dinner plate: $A = \pi r^2 = \pi(5)^2 = 25\pi$; dessert plate: $A = \pi r^2 = \pi(3)^2 = 9\pi$; $25\pi - 9\pi = 16\pi$ in.^{2}

2. 3 to 5, or $\dfrac{3}{5}$

3. 9 to 25, or $\dfrac{9}{25}$

B. r^2 to R^2, or $\dfrac{r^2}{R^2}$

C. **1.** $C = 2\pi r = 2\pi(5) = 10\pi$ in.

2. $\dfrac{C}{A} = \dfrac{10\pi}{25\pi} = \dfrac{2}{5}$

3. $\dfrac{C}{A} = \dfrac{2\pi r}{\pi r^2} = \dfrac{2}{r}$

4. No, since π is a factor in both the numerator and the denominator of the ratio, it can be divided out of the ratio.

Problem 4.3

A. **1.** Check students' work. Side lengths will vary, but angle measures should be 80°, 80°, and 20°.

2. No, the side lengths can vary and still keep the same angle measures.

B. **1.** Check students' work. Angle measures will vary, but the short side should be 6 in. long.

2. No, the lengths of the other two sides of the triangle can be any lengths longer than 3 in.

3. Check students' work. Yes, there is only one possible triangle with a side length of 6 in. and angle measures of 75°, 75°, and 30°.

C. **1.** Check students' work. Only the third triangle is possible to draw.

2. Third triangle; that is the only triangle that can be drawn with the given measures. Its third angle measures 80°.

Check-Up

1. Brahim and Miguel are conducting a survey. They ask the question, "Which sport is your favorite to watch: soccer, basketball, or volleyball?"

   a. Brahim wants to ask 25 of his classmates as they leave a basketball game. Will his results be reliable? Explain.

   b. Miguel wants to ask 1 randomly-selected student from each of 5 gym classes. Will his results be reliable? Explain.

   c. Describe a sampling method Brahim and Miguel could use to have the best chance of producing a representative sample for their survey.

2. Riders on a subway system can get on one of four different subway lines. Rita works for the subway system and wants an accurate prediction of how many of the 10,000 riders who use the station each day take each line.

   a. Rita watches where 10 riders go, and sees that 2 take the green line. Based on Rita's sample, how many riders would you predict take the green line each day? Explain your reasoning.

   b. Rita watches the next 10 riders, and sees that 6 of them take the green line. Based on this sample, how many riders would you predict take the green line each day? Explain your reasoning.

   c. Rita takes a third sample, of 200 riders, and sees that 70 of them take the green line. Based on this sample, how many riders would you predict take the green line each day? Explain your reasoning.

   d. Were your estimates different? If so, explain why they were different. Tell which estimate you think is most accurate and explain your reasoning.

Check-Up *(continued)*

3. Sarah and DeShawn work part-time at the bowling alley. The box plots show the number of hours they have worked each week this year.

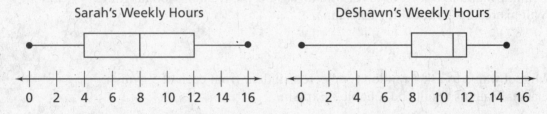

Sarah's Weekly Hours   DeShawn's Weekly Hours

a. Find the ranges and interquartile ranges of the hours Sarah and DeShawn have worked, and use them to compare how their hours varied.

b. Compare how the amounts of hours Sarah and DeShawn worked are distributed.

c. Does either box plot show clustering or symmetry of data? If so, what does that show about the numbers of hours worked?

4. The dot plots show the numbers of texts, to the nearest 10, some students sent one week in the summer and one week during the school year.

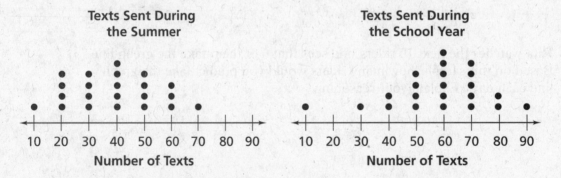

Texts Sent During
the Summer

Number of Texts

Texts Sent During
the School Year

Number of Texts

a. What comparisons can you draw from looking at the plots about the numbers of texts sent during each time of year?

b. What is the difference in the median value for each set of data?

c. For which set of data would you expect a greater interquartile range? Explain your answer.

CC Investigation 5: Variability

© **DOMAIN:** Statistics and Probability

You can collect data from a random sample of a given population and use that data to make inferences about the population as a whole. Inferences will be valid only if the sample is representative of the population.

A sample is **representative** if every member of the population has an equal chance of being included in the sample. Random sampling is the best way to produce a representative sample that will support valid inferences.

Problem 5.1

A. The owners of the Casual Café and the Bountiful Bistro want to know more about the types of customers that dine at their restaurants. They each conduct a survey to find their customers' ages and the price they would expect to pay for an entrée.

1. Suppose the owners took their samples by surveying the first fifteen women dressed in business attire. Do you think this sample is representative of the population? Explain.

2. Suppose the owners took their samples by surveying every fifth customer at lunch. Do you think this sample is representative of the population? Explain.

3. Describe a survey method that would give the restaurant owners a representative sample of the population. Explain how you decided on your method.

B. The table shows age data the owners gathered from a representative sample at each restaurant.

Casual Café	34	41	45	67	23	19	45	34	32	35	34	56	63	23	25
Bountiful Bistro	29	17	23	18	14	28	21	24							

1. What is the mean age for each restaurant's customers? What do the mean ages tell you about the customers that each restaurant attracts?

2. The owners are deciding how to advertise their restaurants. They want to advertise to the group of customers that they expect will want to dine with them. Give some recommendations to each owner about how and where they should advertise.

Notes

C. Diners at Casual Café can make their own sandwiches starting with 1 of 6 fillings.

Make-Your-Own Sandwiches
1. Roast beef
2. Ham
3. Turkey
4. Grouper
5. Veggie
6. Hummus

   1. If the sandwiches are randomly chosen, how many turkey sandwiches do you expect there will be in the next 10 sandwich orders? Explain how you found your answer.

   2. Do an experiment to test your conclusion. Toss a number cube 10 times and record the outcomes in a table. Did the number of times you tossed a 3 match your prediction for the number of turkey sandwiches ordered? Explain why or why not.

   3. How many turkey sandwiches would you expect out of the next 50 random sandwich orders? Do another experiment to test this conclusion. Toss a number cube 50 times and record the outcomes in a table.

   4. Repeat the experiment for another 50 tosses. Record the outcomes in a separate table.

   5. Were the experiments' outcomes closer to your predictions for 10 orders or for 50 orders? Explain why that might be so.

Notes _____

_____

_____

_____

You can use measures of variability, measures of center, and shape to compare the data displayed in two related graphs.

Problem 5.2

Tim is on the wait staff at the Casual Café, and Dan is on the wait staff at Bountiful Bistro. The box plots below display the amounts they earned in tips on weekends during the past six months.

Tim's Earnings (in dollars)

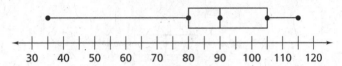

Dan's Earnings (in dollars)

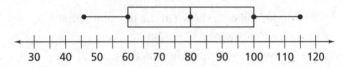

A. What is the range and interquartile range of the data displayed in each box plot?

B. Use the ranges and interquartile ranges of Tim's and Dan's tips. Compare how their tips vary.

C. Are either of the box plots symmetric?

D. Compare how the amounts of Tim's and Dan's tips are distributed.

E. Which, if any, of the box plots shows clusters of data?

F. Use the evidence of clusters or no clusters to compare Tim's and Dan's tips.

G. Overall, who do you think earns more tip money? Explain.

Notes _____

_____

_____

_____

You can use measures of variability, such as interquartile range and mean absolute deviation, to make sense of data sets, both numerically and visually.

Problem 5.3

A. The box plot compares the dinner ticket amounts for the two restaurants.

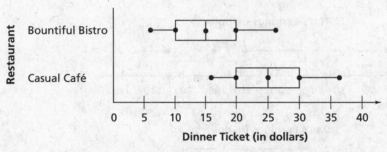

Total Per-Diner Dinner Ticket

1. Compare the distributions of the data shown in the box plot. What conclusions can you draw about the cost of dinner?

2. **a.** Find the median value and the interquartile range for each restaurant.

   b. What is the difference in the medians?

3. Do the results you found support the conclusions you made about the data? Explain why or why not.

B. The dot plots show the lengths of time, to the nearest 10 minutes, some diners spent at dinner at each restaurant.

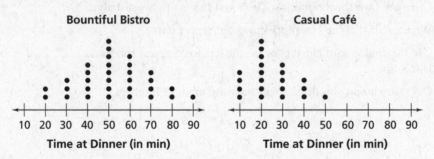

1. What comparisons can you draw from looking at the plots about the time diners spend having dinner at the restaurants?

2. What is the difference in the median value for each set of data?

3. For which set of data would you expect a greater interquartile range? Explain your answer.

STUDENT PAGE

Notes _____

_____

_____

_____

Exercises

For Exercises 1–4, tell whether the sample is representative of the population.

1. You want to know what type of music students at your school like best. You ask a group of your friends which music they like best.

2. You want to know which type of food students at your school like best. You ask every 20th student in your school yearbook.

3. You want to know how many hours students at your school spend on the computer each day. You ask students from different grades as they leave school.

4. You want to know how many hours students at your school exercise each week. You ask the members of the soccer team how often they exercise each week.

5. Suppose you are taking a poll of students in your grade to see whom they are going to select in the election for president of your class. Describe one way you could find a sample that is representative of the population.

6. A student is trying to determine the average length of a song in her large music library. She randomly selects 20 songs and finds that the mean length is 4 minutes 9 seconds. Then, she randomly selects another 20 songs and finds that the mean length is 3 minutes 52 seconds. What would you expect the mean length of a third set of 20 songs would be? Why?

Notes